TRINITY
COLLEGE LONDON PRESS

GRADE

06

SINGING
LOW VOICE

Songs & Teaching Notes for
Trinity College London
Exams 2018–2021

Includes CD of
piano accompaniments
and pronunciation guides

Published by
Trinity College London Press
trinitycollege.com

Registered in England
Company no. 09726123

Printed in England by Caligraving Ltd.

She Moved through the Fair

Padraic Colum
(1881-1972)
Adapted from an old ballad from Co. Donegal

Trad.
arr. Hughes
(1882-1937)

young love said to me,_____ "My_ mo-ther won't mind And my fa - ther_____ won't slight you for your lack of kind,"_____ And she stepped_____ a-way from me and this she did say, "It_____ will not be long, love,_____ till_ our wed-ding day."

She_____ stepped a - way from me_____ and she went thro' the fair, And_fond-ly_____ I watched her move here and move there,_____ And then she_____ went home-ward with one star a - wake, As the_ swan in the eve - ning_____ moves o - ver the lake._____ Last_____

night she came to me___ she came soft-ly in,___ So__ soft-ly___ she

came that her feet made no din,___ And she laid her___ hand on me and this she did

say,___ "It___ will not be long, love,___ till__ our wed-ding

day."___

Das Veilchen

*A violet stood in the meadow, hunched over and unknown; it was a lovely violet. Along came a young shepherdess
with a light step and lively manner, singing. Oh, if only I were the most beautiful of nature's flowers, thought the violet.
It would only be a little while until the sweetheart picked me and held me to her bosom, if only for a quarter of an hour.
Oh dear, oh dear! Without taking care, the girl stepped on the poor violet.
It sank and died yet was happy – so I am dying, through her,
at her feet. The poor violet. It was a lovely violet.*

Johann Wolfgang von Goethe
(1749–1832)

Wolfgang Amadeus Mozart
(1756–1791)

Ein Veil-chen auf der Wie-se stand, ge-bückt in sich und un-be-kannt; es war ein

her - zigs Veil - chen. Da kam ein' jun - ge Schä - fe-rin mit leich - tem Schritt und

mun - term Sinn da - her, da - her, die Wie-se__ her, und__ sang.

5

Ach! denkt das Veil - chen,

wär ich nur die schön-ste Blu-me der Na - tur, ach! nur___ ein klein-es Weil-chen, bis

mich das Lieb-chen ab-gep-flückt, und an dem Bu-sen matt ge-drückt, ach!

nur, ach! nur ein Vier-tel-stünd-chen lang. Ach! a - ber

sf   p

T'intendo, si, mio cor

I feel it, my heart your fast beat! I know you want to groan, the lover that you are.

Ah! Conceal your pain. Ah! Bear your torture. Withhold, and do not be unfaithful to my feelings!

Pietro Metastasio
(1698-1782)

Vincenzo Maria Righini
(1756-1812)

ah! ta - ci il tuo do -lor, ah! sof - fri il tuo mar - tir, ta - ci lo, e non tra -dir gli af-fet-ti mie - i.

-dir gli af-fet-ti mie - i.

9

Quand je fus pris au pavillon

When I was taken to the pavilion by my very fair and beautiful lady, I was burnt by the candle like a moth.
I blushed vermillion at the intensity of the spark when I was taken to the pavilion by my very fair and beautiful lady.
If I had been esmerillon or had good wings, I would have escaped from the one who stung me when I was taken to the pavilion!

Duc Charles d'Orléans
(1394-1465)

Reynaldo Hahn
(1874-1947)

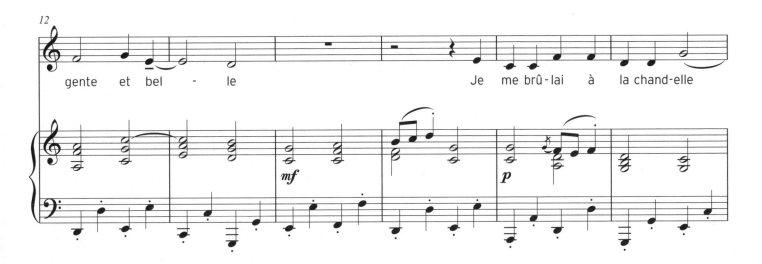

Ain - si que fait___ le pa - pil - lon. Je rou-

-gis com - me ver - mil - lon A la clar - té___ d'une é - tin - cel - le

Quand je fus pris au pa - vil - lon De ma da - me très gente et bel -

- - - le.

Si j'eusse é - té es - me - ril - lon Ou que j'eusse eu aus - si bonne ai - le, Je me fus - se gar - dé de cel - le Qui me bail - la de l'ai-guil - lon Quand je fus pris au pa - vil - lon!

Over the Mountains

from Percy's *Reliques*
(published 1765)

Old English Melody
arr. Quilter
(1877-1953)

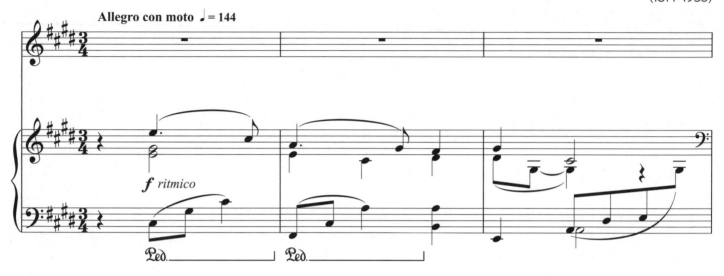

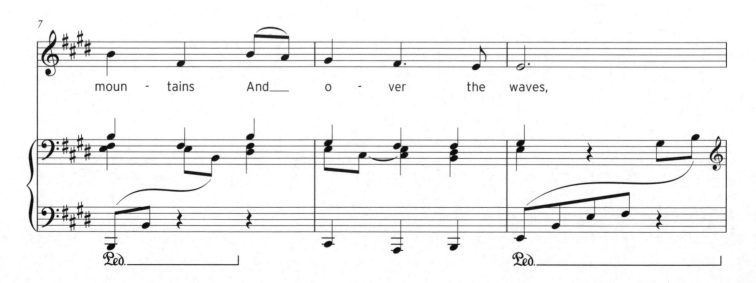

Under the ___ foun - tains And ___ un - der the graves, Un - der floods _____ that are deep - est Which _ Nep - tune o - bey, O - ver rocks that are steep - est, Love will find out the way.

Where there is___ no place For the glow - worm to lie, Where there is___ no space For re - ceipt of a fly: Where the midge_____ dare not ven - ture Lest her - self fast she__ lay, If___ Love come he will en - ter And will

find out the way.

poco dim.

pochiss. riten.   **a tempo**

Some think to lose him Or have him con-

-fined. Some do sup-pose him, Poor thing, to be

blind; But if ne'er so close ye wall him, Do the best that ye

may, Blind Love, if so ye call him, Soon will find out his way.

You may train the eagle To stoop to your fist, Or you may invei-gle The

phoen - ix of the East. The___ lion - ess you may move her To___ get o'er her___ prey, But you'll ne'er stop a lov - er, Love shall find out the way.___

The Cherry Tree

Margaret Rose
(b. 1936)

Cecil Armstrong Gibbs
(1889-1960)

me._____ They sing of the fro - zen riv - ers,____

Pi - ping soft and low_____ Till I

think I hear_____ your___ foot - steps danc - ing

poco rit.   a tempo

a - cross the snow.

The Lamb

William Blake
(1757-1827)

Horace Keats
(1895-1945)

Lit - tle Lamb,_ who made thee?__ Dost thou know_ who

made thee?__ Gave thee life, and bid thee feed By the stream and

Gaeaf

(Winter)

John Lloyd Jones
(1885-1956)

English words: John Stoddart

Dilys Elwyn-Edwards
(1918-2012)

28

hir_____ y bo - re can,_____ Yn or - wych re - dyn__
frost_____ as sil-v'ry ferns_____ Re - peat - ed in__ fair__

poco rit.

a - rian,_____ Em-au'r gwy-dr,_____ ac o, mor gain____ Y__
pat - terns;_____ Gems of bril - liance, rad-iance rare,_____ White

colla voce

bla-gur roes-ai bly-gain!_____
*buds of frost in flo - wer!*_____

Ped._____ Ped.

p

Summer

Alexander McCall Smith
(b. 1948)

Tom Cunningham
(b. 1946)

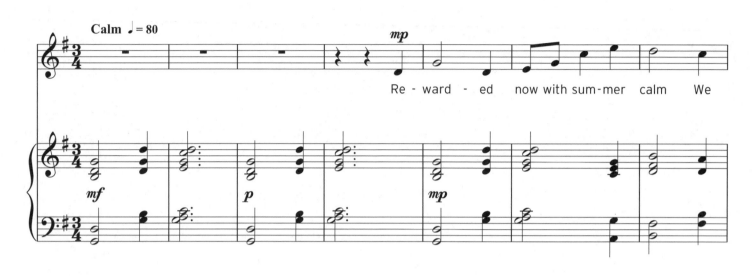

Now Sleeps the Crimson Petal

from *The Princess* by
Alfred, Lord Tennyson
(1809-1892)

Alexander L'Estrange
(b. 1974)

Teaching notes

Trad. *arr.* Hughes   She Moved through the Fair   page 2

In origin this song was a traditional Irish folk song from the county of Donegal, collected and transcribed by the Irish composer Herbert Hughes and the Irish poet and novelist Padraic Colum. Hughes arranged an accompaniment to the original tune while Colum adapted and wrote many of the words. In this version there are only three verses though Colum later added another to stand between verse 2 and verse 3. In this version, without the additional text, there is more of a mystery to the song.

The opening describes the optimism of two young lovers as she reassures him that her family will not mind 'his lack of kind'. This could refer either to the fact that he has no 'kin' or close family or that he does not have much wealth or social standing. He will though be accepted and she promises that they will be married soon. He then watches as she walks away through the 'fair' or the market, likening her beauty to that of a swan. Then comes the more mysterious part as she appears in the night, silently, to reassure him once more that it will not be long before they are married. There is no context for this visitation but the missing verse explains that in fact the lady has died and so it is her ghost that is visiting the lover. The reassurance of the wedding then takes on a different meaning, as there could be a suggestion that the young man too will die soon so they will be united in death.

Hughes has arranged this song in a compound $\frac{6}{4}$ metre and you need both to feel the movement of this two-in-a-bar and to count the rhythms very carefully so as to stay connected to the accompaniment. There should be no feeling of awkwardness in the flow as you sing. In the final verse the accompaniment moves into duplets so you need to be especially careful to ensure a smooth line as you sing in threes against this. This accompaniment and the fact that the verse starts with the piano line lying higher than the voice add to the mysterious feel suggested by the visitation of the ghost so make sure that you sing quietly to enhance the other-worldly atmosphere.

Try and find some recordings of different singers or different versions of this song to see how they portray the meaning.

Mozart   Das Veilchen   page 5

Mozart is one of the most well-known classical composers. He was born in Austria and began writing music from a very early age. He has over 600 compositions to his name in all genres but he particularly loved the sound of the human voice and composed many vocal works including operas, cantatas, masses, concert arias and songs.

This song shows Mozart's keen dramatic instincts. Although relatively short it is full of twists and turns as the story unfolds and you need to narrate all the different episodes with confident characterisation, seeing the tale develop and then conveying it to your listeners. The delicate ornaments in the opening bars should be sung as *appoggiaturas*, gently stressing the first note to suggest the grace of the violet.

Change your tonal colour slightly as the young shepherdess arrives, observing the rests in the phrase to emphasise her lightness of step. Notice how Mozart uses the accompaniment to suggest her singing so, in your performance, imagine that you are listening to her voice as the piano plays. The brief move to the minor key as the violet thinks out loud should be emphasised too as Mozart uses this to suggest that, even though the violet thinks he will be happy, this may not turn out to be the case. And of course, this is true as the maiden unwittingly stamps on the flower. Really bring this section out with some bold singing to match the big chords in the piano part. Use the ensuing pause to give your audience time to assimilate what has happened and then draw out the *rall.* as the violet sinks and dies. This is definitely a 'stage' death! Quicken the pace towards the close before the slow statement of 'Das arme Veilchen' and the much quicker concluding phrase: 'es war ein herzigs Veilchen' which can almost be sung in a cheeky way.

See if you can listen to some other songs by Mozart and think about how he tells different stories using different effects.

Righini   T'intendo, si, mio cor   page 8

The Italian composer, Vincenzo Righini, was born in the same year as Mozart. A gifted singer, he was a chorister in Bologna before studying voice at the Bologna school of singing. He embarked on a professional stage career but soon turned to composition and singing teaching. He is primarily known for his operas.

This song comes from a collection of twelve *ariettas*, or short arias. It is less complicated and elaborate than a true operatic aria but it retains an operatic style and concept. The emotion is heightened as the singer bids the beating heart to be still and to suffer the torment of being in love in silence. The phrases all follow an arched pattern to match this heightening and releasing of emotional tension and so all of them should be sung with this in mind. Although the continuous movement of the accompaniment might suggest a strict tempo there is actually plenty of room for freedom, allowing the sextuplets and other decorative notes to be sung without a sense of urgency or hurry. In order to achieve a shapely line you could imagine drawing a bow across a cello string or drawing a long line on a large piece of canvas, moving with the direction of the music. The highest notes need to be fully connected to the notes preceding them so avoid any sense of reaching for the top notes. Ensure that your chin and shoulders do not lift as you approach any high note as this will introduce unwanted tension and constriction into the sound. Keep the posture strong with the feet firm but almost think of the higher notes as wider notes.

A good way to practise this whole *arietta* might be to sing it to one continuous vowel sound. This way you can really feel the musical line and explore how the sounds stay connected. If you play an instrument you could try playing this as a piece of music. Do you think that this gives you a new perspective on how you might sing it?

Hahn   Quand je fus pris au pavillon   page 11

Reynaldo Hahn was born in Caracas in Venezuela but moved to Paris in France at the age of three. A child prodigy, he was composing from the age of eight and later studied at the Paris Conservatoire under Dubois and Massenet. He was a conductor, music critic and salon singer but he is principally remembered for his vocal music.

Vite, très légèrement as the instruction at the opening of this song means: 'Quick, very light'. Find a speed that allows you to sing suitably quickly but not to sound rushed or as if you are stumbling over the words. Diction needs to be very clear indeed. You could practise by saying the words slowly out loud before trying them out quickly in the rhythms of the song. There are some slightly awkward tied notes, which come on different beats of the bars in different phrases. They need to sound completely natural, without interrupting the flow or the tempo of the music at all. Entries too are not always on the same beat of the bar and you need to be absolutely precise with each one, hitting them exactly on the right beat, neither ahead nor behind. They too should sound natural and not as if they have taken you by surprise! Much of the song lies in a very comfortable register so make sure that the two highest notes of the song, both at the top of a rising fourth, are not snatched or sound strained. Again, slow practice is a good idea to ensure complete integration of these notes. Keep the little grace notes, or *acciaccaturas*, really light and unlaboured. Again, do not allow them to slow the pace.

Absolute precision is called for in this song but it should not sound robotic or unmusical. Are there some vocal exercises you could think of that will help you prepare for a performance? What other songs do you know that are also fast and light?